THE PLAIN JANES

Published by DC Comics,

1700 Broadway,

New York, NY 10019.

Printed in Canada.

DC Comics, a Warner Bros.

Entertainment Company.

ISBN: 1-4012-1115-1

ISBN 13: 978-1-4012-1115-8

3 5989 00048 7259

COVER BY JIM RUGG

Special thanks to the Manhattan and Maplewood MINX Collectives.

THE PLAIN JANES

by CECIL CASTELLUCCI
and JIM RUGG

with lettering by
Jared K. Fletcher

To all you Dandelions.

I KNOW THIS GIRL. I BET HER NAME IS KIM OR ZOË OR CINDY. I USED TO BE THIS GIRL.

IT WOULD BE SO EASY TO SIT WITH HER. I'D BE MADE.

MY WHOLE REER HERE AT BUZZ -DRIN HIGH NGS IN THE BALANCE.

LIKE I CARE.

NO, THANKS.

ONCE UPON A TIME I MIGHT HAVE BEEN TEMPTED. NOT ANYMORE. I WANT SOMETHING DIFFERENT.

EVEN IF IT MEANS GOING IT ALONE.

NO, REALLY, JANE. YOU *WANT* TO SIT WITH US. WE'RE COOL.

NO. IT'S ALL RIGHT. THANKS, THOUGH.

I DON'T THINK YOU *GET* IT.

I GET IT. I'LL JUST SIT OVER HERE. BY *MYSELF.*

HI!

I JUST MOVED HERE.

WHAT ARE YOU READING?

I LIKE YOUR SCARF.

IS THAT A POCKET PROTECTOR?

MY NAME IS JANE.

WHAT'S *YOUR* NAME?

JANE.

JAYNE.

POLLY JANE.

IT'S NOT *THAT* FUNNY.

IT'S PRETTY FUNNY.

TRUST ME. IT'S *NOT*. I AM AN ACTRESS. I AM A *COMEDIENNE*. I KNOW FUNNY. IT'S NOT FUNNY.

I'M STILL LAUGHING ON THE INSIDE.

BRIIING

AREN'T YOUR PARENTS *HAIRDRESSERS?* HOW COULD THEY DO THAT TO YOU?

I CUT IT MYSELF.

THEY DIDN'T LIKE THE CAFÉ I CHOSE. THEY DIDN'T LIKE THE MODERN ART MUSEUM I'D TAKEN THEM TO.

EVER SINCE THE ATTACK, IT FELT LIKE THEY DIDN'T LIKE ANYTHING ABOUT *ME* ANYMORE.

I HAD NOTHING TO SAY TO THEM *EXCEPT* GOODBYE.

WELL, I STILL HAVE A FEW THINGS TO DO AND WE'RE LEAVING EARLY TOMORROW.

ARE YOU GOING TO GO SEE *HIM?* ISN'T THAT CREEPY?

OH, RIGHT. HER SLEEPING *PRINCE.*

SHH. TRY TO BE SENSITIVE

I DIDN'T WANT THEM TALKING ABOUT HIM.

IT WAS SOMETHING THAT THEY DIDN'T UNDERSTAND.

HOW COULD THEY? THEY WEREN'T THERE WHEN THE BOMB WENT OFF.

JOHN DOE WAS.

IT'S NOT THAT I DON'T *LOVE* THEM. I DO. I JUST FEEL LIKE EVERYTHING CRACKED INTO A MILLION PIECES THAT DAY.

MR. HERRARA SAID THAT ODYSSEUS WAS BRAVE AND CLEVER, AND I SAID, *HELL* NO!

HE WAS A COWARD WH HAD TO *HIDE* INSIDE A WOOD HORSE!

I WENT TO THAT DADAIST EXHIBIT YOU MENTIONED IN YOUR SKETCHBOOK.

I GOT A "C" ON THAT MATH TEST I WAS TELLING YOU ABOUT. YOU'D PROBABLY SAY THAT I CAN DO BETTER. I KNOW I CAN.

I'VE JUST BEEN *DISTRACTED.*

I MEAN, REALLY, WHAT IS *IN* THE SECRET CASSEROLE? AND I REALLY *LOVED* WHAT YOU SAID ABOUT SHAKESPEARE IN ENGLISH CLASS, JANE.

OK. I GUESS I'LL MEET YOU AT OUR TABLE. I'M JUST GOING TO GET A VEGETARIAN ENTRÉE.

HI!

I MUST HAVE COOTIES.

OH, *JAAAANE. WE'RE* NOT DOING HOME-WORK.

I'M GOOD HERE, THANKS.

I WAS AFRAID THAT I WOULDN'T MEET ANYONE INTERESTING AT SCHOOL.

AND HERE THEY WERE, MY *TRIBE*, COMPLETELY UNIMPRESSED WITH ME.

Dear John,
I feel like the number one loser at school because even the reject table doesn't want to sit with me.

Too bad, because they seemed like the most interesting people at Buzz Aldrin High.

METRO STYLES
GRAND OPENING
TODAY

METRO STYLES

GRAND OPENING!

I thought maybe I had found some friends.

If only I could get them to talk to me! But they won't even talk to each other.

I just know that these girls, these Janes, are my friends.

I know--

--there are more important things to worry about than making friends.

I'm trying not to let it all bother me. But it does.

I'm lonely for friends.

I miss you. I hope you are getting better. Wake up and write to me.

Love, Jane

P.s. Your sketchbook has given me a great idea.

WHY ARE YOU WEARING A *FAKE* NOSE?

AND WHY DIDN'T YOU DO THE *ASSIGNED* MONOLOGUE?

I'M CYRANO DE BERGERAC.

UHM. YEAH. WE'RE DOING *GREASE*.

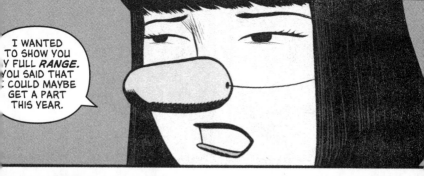

I WANTED TO SHOW YOU MY FULL *RANGE*. YOU SAID THAT I COULD MAYBE GET A PART THIS YEAR.

YOU CAN BE ON STAGE CREW.

NEXT!

P.J., YOU WILL BE TEAM ALTERNATE. GET TO THE BENCH.

YES! BETTER THAN NOTHING.

YOU CAN BE OUR MASCOT AND WEAR THE MOON OUTFIT. THAT MEANS YOU'LL BE WITH THE CHEERLEADERS.

CAN'T I BE AN ALTERNATE, TOO?

TAKE IT OR LEAVE IT.

JANE? IT'S 4 O'CLOCK.

WHERE ARE YOU?

OH NO. IT'S HER MOM.

HA HA HA HA

DO YOU HAVE TO GET PERMISSION FROM YOUR MOM?

HEE

JANE? ARE YOU THERE? PLEASE ANSWER ME SO I KNOW YOU'RE OK.

IT'S FIGHT OR FLIGHT. I PICK FLIGHT.

TAKE ME HOME.

JANE, I'M REALLY STARTING TO WORRY.

THEN, THERE IT WAS IN FRONT OF ME.

A WAY TO MAKE THINGS BEAUTIFUL.

COMING SOON!

NEW STRIP MALL

A CLUB I COULD BELONG TO.

LOTS AVAIL

MOM. I WAS AT *SCHOOL*. SCHOOL *CLUBS* TAKE PLACE AFTER-SCHOOL.

OH, JANE. JUST REMEMBER TO CHECK IN WITH ME.

I'LL BE HOME FOR DINNER. OVER AND OUT.

I COULD JUST PICTURE IT.

ONE DOWN. TWO TO GO.

HARK, WHO *GOES* THERE? OH, 'TIS ONLY *YOU*, JANE. YOU MAY SPEAK IF YOU WISH. I HAVE NOTHING BUT TIME AND *EARS*, AND FOR THE MOMENT THEY ARE YOURS.

I FIGURED THAT JANE WOULD RESPOND TO THE THING THAT SHE LOVED. A TEN-MINUTE THEATRICAL MONOLOGUE TO PLEAD MY CASE.

I HAVE A PLAN.

TAKE A LOOK.

I MUST *ROLL* THE IDEA ABOUT IN MY HEAD.

SO THAT MEANS YOU'LL *THINK* ABOUT IT, RIGHT?

SHE'S HOOKED. SHE TOTALLY SMILING.

SOUNDS LAME.

IT'S GOING TO BE *GREAT.*

CLANG!

P.L.A.I.N. PEOPLE LOVING ART IN NEIGHBORHOODS.

I DUNNO.

ARE YOU GUYS *REALLY* DOING IT?

YES.

I'M GOING TO NEED SOME INCENTIVE.

WE CAN DELAY A PLAYER SO YOU GET TO BE ON THE FIELD AND NOT ON THE BENCH.

IF YOU DO *THAT,* I'M IN.

I FEEL AS THOUGH MY CONTRIBUTIONS TO THE DRAMA CLUB ARE MISUNDERSTOOD.

THEN AGAIN, ALL GENIUS IS MISUNDERSTOOD.

I'M ON EVERY TEAM AT SCHOOL.

MOSTLY I'M THE *BENCHWARMER*.

IT'S BEAUTIFUL.

IT REALLY WORKS.

COOL.

IT'S VERY DRAMATIC. IT'S GOT FLAIR.

I CAN'T WAIT TO HEAR WHAT PEOPLE THINK.

The Pyramids lasted for thousands of years

Do you think this StripMall will?

ART SAVES
THINK BIG
THINK P.L.A.I.N.
(People Loving Art In Neighborhoods)

LOTS AVAILA

he Pyramids
lasted for
usands of years.

you think this
rip Mall will?

ART SAVES
THINK BIG
THINK P.L.A.I.N
(People Loving Art
In Neighborhood

CRAZY KIDS. ASKING FOR PYRAMID POTATOES TODAY, LIKE THEY THINK THAT'S *FUNNY*.

IT'S *NOT* FUNNY.

I FELT INSPIRED.

BUBBLES. DISH WASHING LIQUID IN THE TOWN FOUNTAIN.

I CALCULATE WE'LL NEED AT LEAST TEN LITERS.

I DON'T LOVE ART IN NEIGHBORHOODS. I LOVE *SHOPPING*.

SO--

--CAN I COUNT ON YOU TO BE THERE?

QUESTION IS, CAN I COUNT ON *YOU?*

SO FAR THE ANSWER IS NO.

SO FAR THAT BENCH IS PRETTY *WARM* BECAUSE OF ME.

WELL, I CAN'T SMASH IN SOME-ONE'S KNEE-CAPS.

WHY NOT?

KIDDIN

I JUST WANT TO PLAY.

OH, AND WORK ON YOUR MOONWALK.

IT SUCKS.

I DON'T LIKE IT WHE I FEEL HOPELESS.

HOPELESS IS LYING IN A HOSPITAL BED WITH A RINGING IN YOUR EAR AND TRYING TO FORGET THE SCREAMING.

LOUD NOISES MADE ME JUMP. SOUNDS I COULDN'T IDENTIFY MADE ME JUMP. HELICOPTERS AND SIRENS MADE ME JUMP.

SILENCE MADE ME NERVOUS.

BUT THERE WAS HOPE IN THAT SKETCHBOOK.

WE COULD MAKE THE TOWN AN EXACT *REPLICA* OF OUR SOLAR SYSTEM. A MINI MODEL.

LIKE THOREAU SAID, "WHAT'S THE USE OF A FINE HOUSE IF YOU HAVEN'T GOT A TOLERABLE *PLANET* TO PUT IT ON?"

YEAH. WHAT *SHE* SAID.

BY MY CALCULATIONS, THE SCHOOL CAN BE EARTH SO WE CAN USE THE STATUE OF THE BUZZ AS THE MOON.

WE EACH HAD OUR ASSIGNMENTS.

Dear John,
Did you ever feel so excited about something that you thought your heart would beat right out of your chest?

Of course you have. You're an artist.

Love,
Jane

I'M CALLING THE POLICE. THIS IS OUT OF CONTROL.

THE *POLICE?* ISN'T THAT BEING ALARMIST?

IF THESE ARTISTS CAN SNEAK AROUND AND DO *ATTACKS*, THEN SO CAN PEOPLE WHO WANT TO DO US *HARM*.

YOU OF *ALL* PEOPLE SHOULD KNOW THAT.

PLAIN!

HELLO, 911?

EVERYONE ELSE IN TOWN SEEMS TO KIND OF HAVE A SMILE ON THEIR FACES.

IF ONLY I COULD MAKE HER SEE THE BEAUTY OF IT ALL.

I HAVEN'T HEARD ANYTHING.

HERE'S MY CARD IN CASE YOU *DO* HEAR ANYTHING.

ONE THING WAS CERTAIN.

WE WERE GOING TO HAVE TO BE MORE CAREFUL.

JANE. YOU'RE LATE. WHERE ARE YOU?

I WON'T BE ABLE TO ATTEND THIS EVENING'S FESTIVITIES.

WE NEED YOU, CAN'T YOU SNEAK OUT?

THAT'S HOW I WAS CAUGHT!

I'M GROUNDED. ISN'T THAT *DIVINE!* AT LAST!

I FEEL AS THOUGH I'M GETTING A REAL TEENAGER EXPERIENCE.

THIS IS GOING TO DO *WONDERS* FOR MY SENSE MEMORY. I LIKE TO LOOK AT IT AS A BOON.

WHAT DID YOU TELL THEM?

I TOLD THEM I WAS COMPELLED TO REENACT THE BALCONY SCENE FROM ROMEO AND JULIET. THEY BOUGHT IT, BUT I'M STILL IN TROUBLE.

OH, BROTHER.

I STILL DON'T KNOW. BUT I FEEL BETTER.

SOMEONE'S COMING!

WE'RE BUSTED.

IT'S OVER.

SING?

INSTRUCTIONS FOR FUN AND PLAY IN EVERYDAY LIFE. SING.

OH.

I SAW A POLICE CAR FOUR BLOCKS BACK. I'D CLEAR OUT.

GLOVED HANDS ON THE STEERING WHEEL, TAKING US SOMEWHERE UNCHARTED LIKE OUTER SPACE...

THANKS!

...THE WIPERS ARE BROKEN BUT YOU STILL SEE CLEARLY...

THINGS I KNOW ABOUT DAMON.

HE WEARS VINTAGE JEANS. HE TAKES HOME ECONOMICS. HE DOESN'T HANG AROUND AFTER SCHOOL.

HE ALWAYS SAYS THANK YOU TO THE LUNCH LADY.

HE IS ALWAYS EARLY FOR CLASS. HE WEARS HIS SWEATERS WELL.

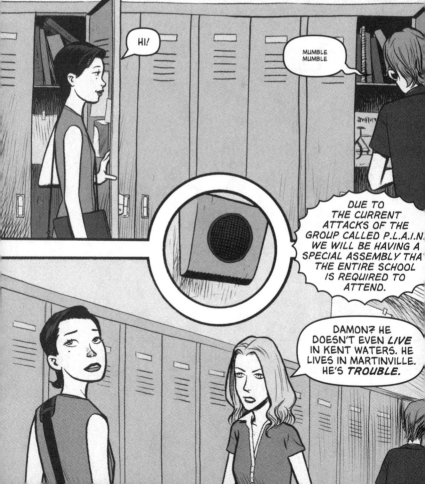

HI!

MUMBLE MUMBLE

DUE TO THE CURRENT ATTACKS OF THE GROUP CALLED P.L.A.I.N. WE WILL BE HAVING A SPECIAL ASSEMBLY THAT THE ENTIRE SCHOOL IS REQUIRED TO ATTEND.

DAMON? HE DOESN'T EVEN *LIVE* IN KENT WATERS. HE LIVES IN MARTINVILLE. HE'S *TROUBLE*.

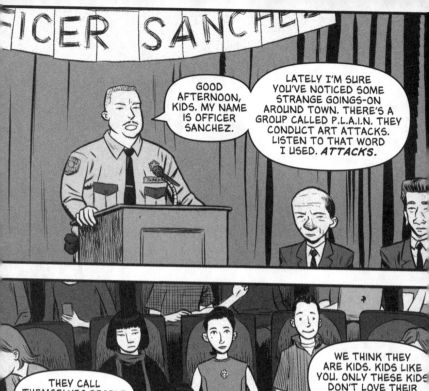

FICER SANCHE

GOOD AFTERNOON, KIDS. MY NAME IS OFFICER SANCHEZ.

LATELY I'M SURE YOU'VE NOTICED SOME STRANGE GOINGS-ON AROUND TOWN. THERE'S A GROUP CALLED P.L.A.I.N. THEY CONDUCT ART ATTACKS. LISTEN TO THAT WORD I USED. *ATTACKS*.

THEY CALL THEMSELVES PEOPLE LOVING ART IN NEIGHBORHOODS.

WE THINK THEY ARE KIDS. KIDS LIKE YOU. ONLY THESE KIDS DON'T LOVE THEIR NEIGHBORHOOD.

THEY DEFACE IT AND THEY CALL IT *ART*. ART IS IN A MUSEUM. NOT ON THE STREETS.

WE AT THE KENT WATERS POLICE DEPARTMENT KNOW THAT YOU KIDS HERE AT BUZZ ALDRIN *DO* LOVE YOUR NEIGHBORHOOD.

THAT'S WHY WE'RE ASKING THAT YOU 'ELP OUR COMMUNITY AND LET US KNOW IF YOU *SEE* OR *HEAR* ANYTHING UNUSUAL.

THE CONSEQUENCES ARE *BIG*.

A JUVENILE RECORD THAT MAY NOT BE EXPUNGED. POSSIBLE *DETENTION* AT A JUVENILE FACILITY. *DEFINITE* COMMUNITY SERVICE.

THIS IS FOR YOUR *PROTECTION*.

I WANT TO *REMIND* ANY OF YOU WHO MAY THINK THAT THESE ART ATTACKS ARE *COOL* THAT *DEFACING* PUBLIC *PROPERTY* IS *NEVER* COOL AND *ALWAYS* ILLEGAL.

THANK YOU.

Dear John,
Sometimes, no matter how hard I try to have fun, I still can't forget about that day, lying next to you on the ground and what happened.

And I worry that art doesn't change anything or anyone.

And I don't want to face the day.

Why is the world still so full of hate?

I can't bear it.

Today nothing is beautiful.
Maybe tomorrow.

Secretly, sometimes I wish I was the one sleeping, and you were the one who was awake.

IT'S LIKE I'M IN EXILE.

JANE.

IS SHE GOING TO LET ME GET MY OWN APARTMENT? GO TO COLLEGE? TRAVEL THE WORLD?

SHE'S SO AFRAID THAT SHE'S GOING TO MAKE *ME* AFRAID OF THE WHOLE UNIVERSE. I DON'T WANT TO BE LIKE THAT.

SHE'S JUST BEING PROTECTIVE.

I'LL TALK TO HER.

SHE'S NOT GETTING BETTER, DAD. SHE'S GETTING *WORSE.*

THERE ARE REASONS THAT I WANT TO GO BACK. ≶CHOKE≶

I KNOW

MAYBE IT'S STIL TOO SOC FOR US

Dear John,

Do you ever feel both happy and miserable at the same time?

NOT ONE OF THEM SAID JANE DOE.

BUT I THOUGHT IT.

IT MUST BE GETTING COLD IN THE CITY.

CITY WORKS

P.L.A.I.N. BUT BEAUTIFUL!

I JUST KNOW IT'S GOING TO BE A LONG WINTER.

HEY.

HEY.

I HAVE SOME TIME TO KILL BEFORE I START WORK.

WANNA GET A COFFEE?

THAT CAFÉ ACROSS THE STREET IS COOL.

I DID. I *DID* WANT TO GET A COFFEE WITH DAMON.

The Loaded Potatoe

MORE THAN ANYTHING.

BUT THERE WAS SOMETHING ABOUT THAT TERRACE. AND THE GARBAGE CAN. AND THE SMELL IN THE AIR.

AND IT WAS THE SAME TIME OF DAY.

SAY YES.

TOO BUSY. PLANS.

I KNOW HE PROBABLY THOUGHT I WAS REJECTING HIM.

SHOOT. MAYBE DAD WAS RIGHT.

I SAID "NO" BECAUSE I WAS AFRAID SOMEONE PUT A BOMB IN THERE.

A P.L.A.I.N.
ANNOUNCEMENT

In which we PLAINly
ask that in advance of
the Thanksgiving holiday,
the town comes together
at the hour of noon on
Wednesday November 23rd
to sing in one voice
the song of their choice.

Sing out. Sing strong.
Sing beautiful.

We love you.

A P.L.A.I.N.
ANNOUCEMENT

In which we PLAINly
ask that in advance of
the Thanksgiving holiday,
the town comes together
at the hour of noon on
Wednesday Novem...
to sing in...

I DON'T GET IT. JANE. YOU'RE KIND OF *ARTY*. DO *YOU* GET IT?

NOPE.

HUNDREDS OF TEENAGERS DANCING.

HUNDREDS OF FEELINGS OF BEING FREE.

I'm so glad I'm P.L.A.I.N.

WHEN THE LINES ARE BEING DRAWN, IT'S SURPRISING TO SEE WHO COMES OUT OF THE WOODWORK TO YELL THE LOUDEST.

YOU. JANES. WHERE ARE YOUR *PINS?*

SEE YOU AT THE PEP RALLY AFTER SCHOOL.

AND JANE? SHOW SOME *SPIRIT.*

BE PROUD YOU ARE P.L.A.I.N.

IT FELT SO GOOD TO CHEER FOR OURSELVES.

BUT PEOPLE WHO HAVE BIG MOUTHS OFTEN GET INTO TROUBLE.

CINDY!

WAIT UP...

...WHAT *HAPPENED* LAST NIGHT?

THERE WAS A PEP RALLY.

NOT THAT.

I SAW YOU GET INTO THAT *COP* CAR.

GOD! I'M SO TIRED OF *QUESTIONS!*

I DON'T ASK *YOU* QUESTIONS, JANE. SO DON'T ASK *ME* ANY.

I'M LATE NOW.

WITH SOME PEOPLE YOU JUST CAN'T WIN.

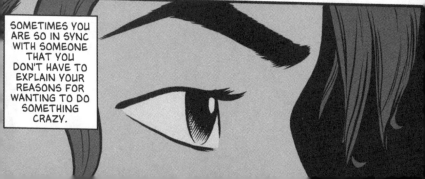

MY PARENTS DIDN'T UNDERSTAND ANYTHING.

MOM. DAD. I *HAD* TO GO. YOU KNOW THAT.

THERE HAVE BEEN ELEVATED *THREATS* AGAINST METRO CITY ALL WEEK!

IT'S NOT SAFE THERE.

The Chronicle
KENT WATERS CANCELS NEW YEARS CLOCK TOWER BALL DROP

I WAS ALL KINDS OF GROUNDED.

NO AFTERSCHOOL ACTIVITIES. NO FRIENDS OVER. NO GOING OUT.

NO PHONE CALLS. NO T' NO COMPUTE

NO COMPUTER? WHY DON'T YOU JUST *KILL* ME?

I HAD TO FIND OUT WHAT *HAPPENED!* BECAUSE I'M A FEELING PERSON!

MOM. DAD. IT'S NOT SAFE *ANYWHERE!* WHY CAN'T YOU JUST *ADMIT* THAT?

IT'S A TRADITION. NEW YEAR'S WON'T BE THE SAME.

HOW HARD CAN IT BE TO DROP A BALL?

THAT'S IT! WE TAKE THE TRADITION INTO OUR *OWN* HANDS!

WE THROW THE BALL OFF THE CLOCK TOWER AT MIDNIGHT.

BUT NO ONE WILL BE THERE TO SEE IT.

UNLESS... WE FILL IT WITH *PAINT*.

AND MAKE IT P.L.A.I.N.

AND ADD GLITTER, RIGHT?

IT'LL BE SO JACKSON POLLOCK.

WAIT, JANE, AREN'T YOU GROUNDED FOR, LIKE, *EVER?*

I JUST THINK WE'RE SUPPOSED TO BE *FRIENDS*.

NO HARD FEELINGS, RIGHT?

BRIIING

COOL.

BOYS SUCK.

BrainJayne: According to many psychological profiles, men don't always behave in a manner that is predictable, ergo, their ACTIONS make no sense.

MainJane: Speak English.

IT'S ALL RIGHT, GIRL. LET IT ALL *OUT*. BOYS SUCK.

ALL I KNOW IS THAT NO MATTER WHAT THEY SAID, MY HEART STILL HURT.

OH L'AMOUR! AVEUGLE ET FOU!

DO YOU WANT ME TO BEAT HIM UP?

BUT YOU KNOW, LIFE GOES ON. AND MY PARENTS GOT SOME HOLIDAY SPIRIT AND LET ME GO OUT A LITTLE BIT.

I HATE SHOPPING. LET'S JUST HURRY UP AND GET OUT OF HERE.

SHOPPING IS FUN! HAVEN'T YOU EVER HEARD OF RETAIL THERAPY?

JANE. WHAT YOU NEED IS A NEW CRUSH.

IT WASN'T JUST A CRUSH. IT WAS DIFFERENT.

EAT CHOCOLATE. IT RELEASES THE SAME CHEMICALS AS LOVE DOES IN THE BRAIN.

WHO NEEDS A STUPID GRAMPA-LOVING, BOOK-READING, GOOD-SMELLING BOY WHO I LIKE TALKING TO?

FIRE DEPT TOY DRIVE

I HAD *REAL* FRIENDS.

IT'S A FACT OF LIFE. HEARTS ARE ALWAYS HURTING.

AND YET THEY STILL KEEP PUMPING.

THE BEST WAY TO FIX A BROKEN HEART IS TO DO SOMETHING BEAUTIFUL. SOMETHING P.L.A.I.N.

I KNEW JUST WHAT TO DO.

P.L.A.I.N. ACTS OF LOVE.

Donate a toy to the Fire Dept

It's P.L.A.I.N. to see you've sent your holiday cards

BUT HAVE YOU OPENED YOUR HEART?

THE JANES WOULD GO TO THE PARTY ALONG WITH EVERY OTHER KID IN THE UNIVERSE.

I WAS THE ONLY PERSON AT BUZZ ALDRIN WHO WASN'T GOING. BUT THAT WAS OK. IT WAS PART OF THE PLAN.

DON'T *TOUCH* THE BROWS.

I'M DOING YOUR HAIR, POLLY JANE. NOT YOUR FACE!

OK, WELL, JUST STAY AWAY FROM THEM.

I *CAN'T* MAKE YOU GLAMOROUS IF YOU'RE READING A *BOOK*.

I'M NOT COMFORTABLE WITH THESE FEMALE BEAUTY RITUALS.

JANE, I CAN'T *WORK* LIKE THIS!

THE GIRLS WOULD TELL PEOPLE THAT THERE WAS GOING TO BE A P.L.A.I.N. ATTACK AT THE CLOCK TOWER AT MIDNIGHT.

WOULD TAKE THE BALL TO THE TOWER AND AT 11:30 THE JANES WOULD COME MEET ME TO HELP WITH THE BALL SMASHING.

AT QUARTER TO MIDNIGHT, THE WHOLE PARTY WOULD WALK FROM CINDY'S HOUSE TO THE TOWN SQUARE.

AT MIDNIGHT WE WOULD BLOW HORNS, THROW GLITTER AND TOSS THE BALL OFF THE CLOCK TOWER.

IT WAS GOING TO BE THE BEST NEW YEAR'S EVER.

BUT NOTHIN
IS EVER EAS
IS IT?

DAMON-- ARE YOU *LEAVING?*

JANE SHOULDN'T BE ALONE. I'M GOING OVER THERE TO HELP HER.

THAT'S *NOT* THE PLAN.

I DON'T CARE.

YOU'RE THE *LAST* PERSON JANE WANTS TO SEE.

I KNOW WE HATE HIM BECAUSE OF HOW LAME HE WAS TO JANE, BUT DAMON'S LIPS ARE *SO KISSABLE.*

THEY SURE ARE.

DAD! WHAT ARE YOU *DOING* HERE?

YOU SAID YOU'D STAY AWAY!

CYNTHIA. I JUST STOPPED BY TO CHECK UP ON YOU.

AND I OVERHEARD SOME KIDS TALKING ABOUT A P.L.A.I.N. ATTACK TONIGHT?

THIS PARTY IS *OVER* UNTIL I GET SOME *ANSWERS.*

DAD. I DON'T KNOW *WHAT* YOU'RE TALKING ABOUT. I *DO* KNOW THAT YOU ARE RUINING MY *LIFE.*

I WANT TO KNOW *WHO.* AND I WANT TO KNOW *WHERE.*

HOLD IT RIGHT THERE.

WHERE ARE YOU GIRLS *GOING?*

I'M GOING TO BE *SICK.* I NEED SOME FRESH AIR.

THERE'S THE BATHROOM. BE SICK IN THERE.

EVERYONE ELSE INTO THE LIVING ROOM.

AND IF YOU DON'T JOIN US A FEW MINUTES YOU'LL *REGRET* IT.

You think you know people. You think you can count on them.

But we're really all alone in this world, aren't we?

Tell me, Miroslaw. If I do something beautiful and no one else sees it, is it still worth doing?

WHERE ARE THEY?

MAYBE THEY'RE HAVING TOO MUCH FUN AT CINDY'S.

MAYBE THEY DON'T LIKE ART ANYMORE.

MAYBE THEY DON'T LIKE *ME* ANYMORE.

MAYBE THEY THINK ART IS STUPID.

I'M OUT OF HERE.

JANE-- WHERE ARE YOU *GOING?*

I DON'T WANT TO BE A MEMBER OF A CLUB THAT DOESN'T WANT ME.

SO, YOU'RE GIVING *UP?*

THERE'S ALWAYS THIS EXPECTATION ON NEW YEAR'S EVE.

AND THEN IT'S A LETDOWN.

I THOUGHT THIS YEAR WOULD BE DIFFERENT.

WELL, IT'S ALMOST *MIDNIGHT.*

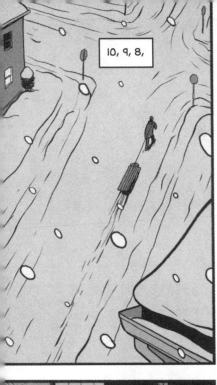

DAD!

LET ME SEE THE PAPER.

THEY CAUGHT THAT ARTIST.

IT'S SOME BOY FROM YOUR SCHOOL.

DID YOU KNOW HIM? HE'S BEING SUSPENDED.

P.L.A.I.N. ARTIST CAUGHT !!

A sophomore student from Buzz Aldrin High was caught at the scene of the clocktower dropping a ball

Sanchez said, "It's a relief for the town to get the culprit off the streets. Mr Sheinberg thought that he

The End.

CECIL CASTELLUCCI

Cecil grew up in New York City, is French Canadian and makes her home in Los Angeles. She's the author of three young adult novels, *Boy Proof*, *The Queen of Cool*, and the upcoming *Beige*. Cecil is also an indie rock musician, an independent filmmaker and a playwright. During her years at the LaGuardia High School of Performing Arts, she'd see Keith Haring's drawings in the subways in New York. She still looks for street art whenever she's on a walk.

JIM RUGG

Jim is the artist and co-creator of *Street Angel*. His comics have also appeared in anthologies including *Project: Superior, SPX, Orchid*, and *Meathaus*. He grew up near Pittsburgh and hasn't come up with a good excuse to skip town. He's disappointed his school didn't have a girl gang like the Janes or the Dagger Debs.

SPECIAL BACKSTAGE PASS:

If you liked the story you've just read, fear not: other MINX

books will be available in the months to come. MINX is a line

of books that's designed especially for you — someone who's

a bit bored with straight fiction and ready for

stories that are visually exciting beyond words — literally.

In fact, we thought you might like to get in on a secret,

behind-the-scenes look at a few of the new MINX titles that

will aid in your escape to cool places during the long hot

summer. So hurry up and turn the page already! And be

sure to check out other exclusive material at

minxbooks.net

A Korean-American California girl who's into

martial arts learns that in romance and recycled gifts,

what goes around comes around.

COMING IN JUNE 2007 ■ Read on.

IT'S TRUE THAT I HAVE VERY **POWERFUL** EMOTIONS.

I DON'T **SHOW** IT, BUT DEEP DOWN I'M A **REALLY** PASSIONATE PERSON.

SHE'S AS SPIKY AS A **PORCUPINE**.

THAT'S ONE OF THE **TWO** REASONS WHY I DO HAPKIDO. IT'S AN **OUTLET** FOR ME.

BECAUSE I DON'T FIND IT **EASY** TO EXPRESS WHAT I FEEL IN **WORDS**.

SHE GETS TO BEAT PEOPLE **UP**.

SHE REALLY **LIKES** BEATING PEOPLE UP.

HEY, THIS IS **MY** STORY, AVRIL! IS THAT YOUR VOICE IN THE CAPTION BOX? DOESN'T LOOK LIKE IT TO **ME**!

DIDN'T SAY A **WORD**. SORRY.

ZZZIP

EIGHTY-FIVE. NINETY-FIVE. ONE HUNDRED.

PUT THIS IN YOUR MONEY BOX *IMMEDIATELY*, JEN. AND GIVE IT TO MASTER *CHOI* TOMORROW.

YES, OPPA.

NOT *FAIR!*

I NEED A NEW *BIKE*-- ONE I CAN RIDE WITHOUT MY *KNEES* HITTING ME IN THE CHIN.

AND I WANT A *BASKETBALL HOOP* (BUT I'LL SETTLE FOR *CASH*).

MICKEY. SOON. YOU KNOW THAT WE DON'T HAVE MUCH *MONEY* SINCE SA-I-GU.*

YEAH.

SO?

AND HAPKIDO IS A VERY *HIGH* PRIORITY, SECOND ONLY AFTER *SCHOOL.*

*WHAT KOREANS CALL THE RODNEY KING RIOTS--LITERALLY "APRIL 29TH".

A spoiled, rebellious Londoner conquers the

stuffy English countryside when she solves a

murder mystery on the 19th hole of her grandparents'

golf course.

The girl there, gabbing on the Razr, the one who looks like a silent movie star wearing dissolution lip gloss? That's me.
Cute, aren't I? People think so until I open my mouth. My mum's always saying I'm so sharp I'll cut myself.
Anyway, that's me in happier times.
Before I was exiled.
CHARLOTT BROOK.

Meadowdale missed me—that's for sure. It was what—at least three years since I graced those country lanes.

CHARLOTTE, MY DEAR GIRL.

But I didn't have to put on a front.

GRANDMA AGGIE.

I was genuinely glad to see her. Here's an adult who isn't shouting at me.

Yet.

IT'S SO LOVELY TO SEE YOU.

One thing you never forget about Gran, she's tactile.

One crushed larynx and seven cracked vertebrae later...

WELCOME TO THE LAKE DISTRICT.

Derek Kirk Kim & Jesse Hamm

Good As Lily

What would you do if versions of yourself at ages 6, 29 and 70 suddenly became part of your already complicated high school life?

Grace, Grace! Are you okay?

Grace, say something!

Hey, can you hear us?

Uuuhh, yeah, yeah, I'm fine. Stop yelling, I--

What the--?! Why can't I see anything? I can't *see*!! *I'm bliiiiind!!*

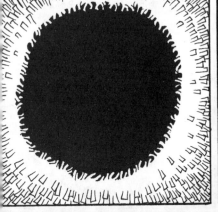

So there I was, about to blow my stack. But as I looked at the three of them, I suddenly started to feel dizzy. The total craziness of what was before me was hitting me full force again. There I was, standing in my room with... myself... at the age of 6, 29, and 70. I felt like I was in a dream, surrounded by distorted mirrors in an impossible funhouse.

...I can't stop staring... My room... My old room...

Okay, I wanna know one thing. What happened on your 18th birthday after you got hit on the head with the piñata?

I never had a piñata on my 18th birthday...

Yeah, what piñata?

Don't miss any of the upcoming books of 2007:

CONFESSIONS OF A BLABBERMOUTH
By Mike and Louise Carey and Aaron Alexovich
September

When Tasha's mom brings home a creepy boyfriend and his deadpan daughter, a dysfunctional family is headed for a complete mental meltdown.

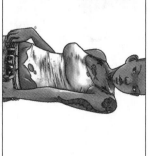

Ross Campbell

WATER BABY
By Ross Campbell
October

Surfer girl Brody just got her leg bitten off by a shark. What's worse? Her shark of an ex-boyfriend is back, and when it comes to Brody's couch, he's not budging.

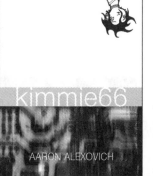

KIMMIE66
By Aaron Alexovich
November

This high-velocity, virtual reality ghost story follows a tech-savvy teenager on a dangerous quest to save her best friend, the world's first all-digital girl.

Go to
minxbooks.net
for exclusive interviews
and bonus artwork!

The Face of Modern Fictio